Nursery Rhymes
for Young Australians

Illustrated by Jan Wade

LIFETIME DISTRIBUTORS
"The Book People"

Published by National Book Distributors Pty Ltd
3/2 Aquatic Drive, Frenchs Forest, NSW 2086

This edition distributed in Australia by
Lifetime Distributors, Unit 6/8, Victoria Avenue
Castle Hill, NSW 2154

First published in 1990, reprinted 1991, 1993, 1995 (twice)

Copyright © in text and artwork National Book Distributors Pty Ltd, 1995

Illustrations by Jan Wade

Typeset in Australia by Deblaere Typesetting Pty Ltd
Printed and bound in Hong Kong by Everbest Printing Co., Ltd.

ISBN 1 86436 087 9

Contents

HUMPTY DUMPTY

Humpty Dumpty sat on a wall,
Humpty Dumpty had a great fall;
All the King's horses and all the King's men
Couldn't put Humpty together again.

BAA, BAA, BLACK SHEEP

Baa, baa, black sheep,
  Have you any wool?
Yes, sir, yes, sir,
  Three bags full;

One for the master,
  And one for the dame,
And one for the little boy
  Who lives down the lane.

9

JACK AND JILL

Jack and Jill
Went up the hill,
To fetch a pail of water;
Jack fell down,
And broke his crown,
And Jill came tumbling after.

Then up Jack got,
And home did trot,
As fast as he could caper;
He went to bed,
To mend his head
With vinegar and brown paper.

When Jill came in,
How she did grin
To see Jack's paper plaster;
Her mother, vexed,
Did whip her next,
For laughing at Jack's disaster.

Now Jack did laugh
And Jill did cry,
But her tears did soon abate;
Then Jill did say,
That they should play
At see-saw across the gate.

LITTLE BOY BLUE

Little Boy Blue,
  Come blow your horn,
The sheep's in the meadow,
  The cow's in the corn.

Where is the boy
  Who looks after the sheep?
He's under the haystack
  Fast asleep.

Will you wake him?
  No, not I,
For if I do,
  He's sure to cry.

THE CAT AND THE FIDDLE

Hey diddle, diddle,
The cat and the fiddle,
The cow jumped over the moon;
The little dog laughed
To see such sport,
And the dish ran away with the spoon.

13

THE MISCHIEVOUS RAVEN

A farmer went trotting upon his grey mare,
   Bumpety, bumpety, bump!
With his daughter behind him so rosy and fair,
   Lumpety, lumpety, lump!

A raven cried, Croak! and they all tumbled down,
   Bumpety, bumpety, bump!
The mare broke her knees and the farmer his crown,
   Lumpety, lumpety, lump!

The mischievous raven flew laughing away,
   Bumpety, bumpety, bump!
And vowed he would serve them the same the next day,
   Lumpety, lumpety, lump!

LITTLE BO-PEEP

Little Bo-peep has lost her sheep,
   And doesn't know where to find them;
Leave them alone, and they'll come home,
   Bringing their tails behind them.

Little Bo-peep fell fast asleep,
   And dreamt she heard them bleating;
But when she awoke, she found it a joke,
   For they were still a-fleeting.

Then up she took her little crook,
   Determined for to find them;
She found them indeed, but it made her heart bleed
   For they'd left their tails behind them.

It happened one day, as Bo-peep did stray
   Into a meadow hard by,
That she espied their tails side by side,
   All hung on a tree to dry.

She heaved a sigh, and wiped her eye,
   And over the hillocks went rambling,
And tried what she could, as a shepherdess should,
   To tack again each to its lambkin.

THIS LITTLE PIG

This little pig went to market,
This little pig stayed home,

This little pig had roast beef,
This little pig had none,
And this little pig cried, Wee-wee-wee-wee-wee,
All the way home.

THE THREE LITTLE KITTENS

Three little kittens
They lost their mittens,
And they began to cry,
  Oh, Mother dear,
  We sadly fear
  Our mittens we have lost,
What! lost your mittens,
You naughty kittens!
Then you shall have no pie.
  Mee-ow, mee-ow, mee-ow.
No, you shall have no pie.

The three little kittens
They found their mittens,
And they began to cry,
  Oh, Mother dear,
  See here, see here,
  Our mittens we have found.
Put on your mittens,
You silly kittens,
And you shall have some pie.
  Purr-r, purr-r, purr-r,
  Oh, let us have some pie.

The three little kittens
Put on their mittens
And soon ate up the pie;
  Oh, Mother dear,
  We greatly fear
  Our mittens we have soiled.
What! soiled your mittens,
You naughty kittens!
  Then they began to sigh,
  Mee-ow, mee-ow, mee-ow,
  Then they began to sigh.

The three little kittens
They washed their mittens,
And hung them out to dry;
  Oh, Mother dear,
  Do you not hear,
  Our mittens we have washed.
What! washed your mittens,
Then you're good kittens,
But I smell a rat close by.
  Mee-ow, mee-ow, mee-ow,
  We smell a rat close by.

17

THE HOUSE THAT JACK BUILT

This is the house
  That Jack built.

This is the malt
That lay in the house
  That Jack built.

This is the rat,
That ate the malt
That lay in the house
  That Jack built.

This is the cat,
That killed the rat,
That ate the malt
That lay in the house
  That Jack built.

This is the dog,
That worried the cat,
That killed the rat,
That ate the malt
That lay in the house
  That Jack built.

This is the cow with the crumpled horn,
That tossed the dog,
That worried the cat,
That killed the rat,
That ate the malt
That lay in the house
  That Jack built.

This is the maiden all forlorn,
That milked the cow with the crumpled horn,
That tossed the dog,
That worried the cat,
That killed the rat,
That ate the malt
That lay in the house
  That Jack built.

This is the man all tattered and torn,
That kissed the maiden all forlorn,
That milked the cow with the crumpled horn,
That tossed the dog,
That worried the cat,
That killed the rat,
That ate the malt
That lay in the house
  That Jack built.

This is the priest all shaven and shorn,
That married the man all tattered and torn,
That kissed the maiden all forlorn,
That milked the cow with the crumpled horn,
That tossed the dog,
That worried the cat,
That killed the rat,
That ate the malt
That lay in the house
  That Jack built.

This is the cock that crowed in the morn,
That waked the priest all shaven and shorn,
That married the man all tattered and torn,
That kissed the maiden all forlorn,
That milked the cow with the crumpled horn,
That tossed the dog,
That worried the cat,
That killed the rat,
That ate the malt
That lay in the house
  That Jack built.

This is the farmer sowing his corn,
That kept the cock that crowed in the morn,
That waked the priest all shaven and shorn,
That married the man all tattered and torn,
That kissed the maiden all forlorn,
That milked the cow with the crumpled horn,
That tossed the dog,
That worried the cat,
That killed the rat,
That ate the malt
That lay in the house
  That Jack built.

This is the horse and the hound and the horn,
That belonged to the farmer sowing his corn,
That kept the cock that crowed in the morn,
That waked the priest all shaven and shorn,
That married the man all tattered and torn,
That kissed the maiden all forlorn,
That milked the cow with the crumpled horn,
That tossed the dog,
That worried the cat,
That killed the rat,
That ate the malt
That lay in the house
  That Jack built.

GIRLS AND BOYS COME OUT TO PLAY

Girls and boys come out to play,
The moon doth shine as bright as day!

Leave your supper and leave your sleep,
Come with your playfellows into the street.

Come with a whistle, come with a call,
Come with a good will or come not at all.

Up the ladder and down the wall,
A halfpenny roll will serve us all.

You find the milk and I'll find flour,
And we'll have pudding in half an hour.

LITTLE MISS MUFFET

Little Miss Muffet
Sat on a tuffet,
Eating her curds and whey;

There came a big spider,
Who sat down beside her
And frightened Miss Muffet away.

OLD MOTHER HUBBARD

Old Mother Hubbard
Went to the cupboard,
To fetch her poor dog a bone;
But when she got there
The cupboard was bare
And so the poor dog had none.

She went to the baker's
    To buy him some bread;
But when she came back
    The poor dog was dead.

She went to the undertaker's
    To buy him a coffin;
But when she came back
    The poor dog was laughing.

She took a clean dish
    To get him some tripe;
But when she came back
    He was smoking a pipe.

She went to the fishmonger's
    To buy him some fish;
But when she came back
    He was licking the dish.

She went to the tavern
    For white wine and red;
But when she came back
    The dog stood on his head.

She went to the fruiterer's
  To buy him some fruit;
But when she came back
  He was playing the flute.

She went to the tailor's
  To buy him a coat;
But when she came back
  He was riding a goat.

She went to the hatter's
  To buy him a hat;
But when she came back
  He was feeding the cat.

She went to the barber's
  To buy him a wig;
But when she came back
  He was dancing a jig.

She went to the cobbler's
  To buy him some shoes;
But when she came back
  He was reading the news.

She went to the seamstress
  To buy him some linen;
But when she came back
  The dog was a-spinning.

She went to the hosier's
  To buy him some hose;
But when she came back
  He was dressed in his clothes.

The dame made a curtsey,
  The dog made a bow;
The dame said, Your servant,
  The dog said, Bow-wow.

THE OWL AND THE PUSSY CAT

The Owl and the Pussy-Cat went to sea
  In a beautiful pea-green boat,
They took some honey, and plenty of money,
  Wrapped up in a five pound note.
The Owl looked up to the stars above,
  And sang to a small guitar,
'O lovely Pussy! O Pussy, my love,
  What a beautiful Pussy you are,
    You are,
    You are,
What a beautiful Pussy you are!'

Puss said to the Owl, 'You elegant fowl!
  How charmingly sweet you sing!
O let us be married! too long we have tarried:
  But what shall we do for a ring?'
They sailed away for a year and a day,
  To the land where the Bong-tree grows,
And there in a wood a Piggy-wig stood,
  With a ring at the end of his nose,
    His nose,
    His nose,
  With a ring at the end of his nose.

'Dear Pig, are you willing to sell for one shilling,
  Your ring?' Said the piggy, 'I will.'
So they took it away, and were married next day
  By the Turkey who lived on the hill.
They dined on mince, and slices of quince,
  Which they ate with a runcible spoon;
And hand in hand, on the edge of the sand,
They danced by the light of the moon,
  The moon,
  The moon,
They danced by the light of the moon.

Edward Lear

ONE, TWO, THREE, FOUR, FIVE

One, two, three, four, five,
Once I caught a fish alive,
Six, seven, eight, nine, ten,
Then I let it go again.
Why did you let it go?
Because it bit my finger so.
Which finger did it bite?
The little finger on the right.

MR NOBODY

I know a funny little man,
  As quiet as a mouse.
He does the mischief that is done
  In everybody's house.
Though no one ever sees his face,
  Yet one and all agree
That every plate we break, was cracked
  By Mr Nobody.

'Tis he who always tears our books,
  Who leaves the door ajar.
He picks the buttons from our shirts,
  And scatters pins afar.
That squeaking door will always squeak —
  For prithee, don't you see?
We leave the oiling to be done
  By Mr Nobody.

He puts damp wood on the fire,
  That kettles will not boil;
His are the feet that bring in the mud
  And all the carpets soil.
The papers that so oft are lost —
  Who had them last but he?
There's no one tosses them about
  But Mr Nobody.

The fingermarks upon the door
  By none of us were made.
We never leave the blinds unclosed
  To let the curtains fade.
The ink we never spill! The boots
  That lying round you see,
Are not our boots — they all belong
  To Mr Nobody.

27

THREE MEN IN A TUB

Rub-a-dub-dub,
Three men in a tub,
And who do you think they be?
The butcher, the baker,
The candlestick-maker,
Push them out, one two three.

ROCK-A-BYE

Rock-a-bye, baby, on the tree top,
When the wind blows the cradle will rock;
When the bough breaks the cradle will fall,
And down will come baby, cradle, and all.